One Thing.
Done!

The Simplest Strategy for Acheiving Success in
Every Aspect of Your Life

This Sellinger Group Publication Edition is published by

Victor Antonio of the Sellinger Group.

Contact Information:

PO Box 4342,

Alpharetta, GA 30023

VictorAntonio.com

Printed in the United States of America First Printing: May 2024

Library of Congress Cataloging in Publication Data

Antonio, Victor

One Thing. Done!

ARE YOU READY TO MOVE FORWARD?

BIG GOAL

What's one **Big Goal** you want to accomplish in 30 days?

INSTRUCTIONS

STEP 01

BIG GOAL

Increase revenue by 15% in 30 days by selling new line of products.

Every day write down 1 task toward your big goal. Flip your band to the Red side.

STEP 02

Make 5 calls to new leads

Get 1 thing done everyday. Write it down and check it off when you're done.

STEP 03

DONE!

Flip your wristband from red 'One Thing" to green "DONE!" when you've finshed the days task. Repeat for 30 days.

DAY 22	DAY 21	DAY 20	DAY 19	DAY 18	DAY 17	DAY 16

DAY 23		DAY 15

BIG GOAL

DAY 24		DAY 14

DAY 25		DAY 13

DAY 26		DAY 12

DAY 27		DAY 11

DAY 28		DAY 10

DAY 29		DAY 9

FINISH | | DAY 8 |

START	DAY 2	DAY 3	DAY 4	DAY 5	DAY 6	DAY 7

DAY1

One thing to get done...

DAY 2

One thing to get done...

DAY 3

You landed on a Reward Day!

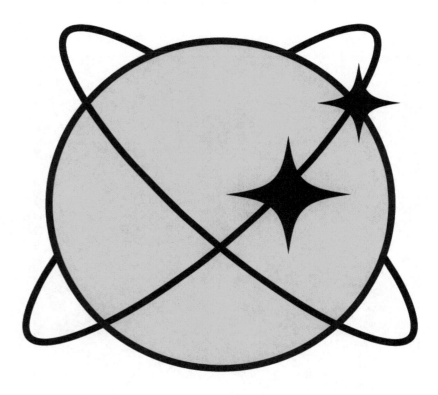

Go for a walk or go somewhere fun and pat yourself on the back for crushing your goals!

DAY 3

One thing to get done...

DAY 4

One thing to get done...

START QUESTIONING WHY

Five monkeys were put in a room where experimenters could observe them through a two-way mirror. In the middle of the room was a staircase and atop the staircase there dangled a banana from a rope. Now every time one of the monkeys began to climb the stairs to retrieve the banana, they were blasted with a high-pressure hose. Eventually the monkeys learned that if any one of them approached the stairs all five would get blasted with water. So after a while none of the monkeys dared venture near the staircase.

The first phase of the conditioning experiment was complete. The experimenter then replaced one of the monkeys with a new monkey. The new monkey, having never experienced the hose, tried to approach the stairs to get the banana only to be beaten back by the other four original monkeys. Every time the new monkey tried, the original monkeys beat him back.

Eventually the new monkey learned to stay away from the stairs. They then replaced another original monkey with new monkey. And the same thing happened. The original monkeys and the new monkey beat the latest addition back until he learned not to approach the stairs. The experimenters continued to replace the original monkeys with a new monkey until all five had been replaced.

The odd thing was that even though none of the five new monkeys had never experience the hose, they continue to beat back anyone who tried to get near the stairs. If you could ask them, "Why do you do it?" They would probably reply, "I don't know; it's always been done that way."

The killer of innovation and advancement is saying, "I don't know; it's always been done that way." The ability to bring about change, in your job or your life, begins with awareness and a curiosity to question why you do what you do as opposed to simply accepting things as they are.

We are all creatures of habits and routines but once in a while, you need to stop and ask yourself, "Why am I doing this? Is there a better way?" and, stop monkeying around!

DAY5

One thing to get done...

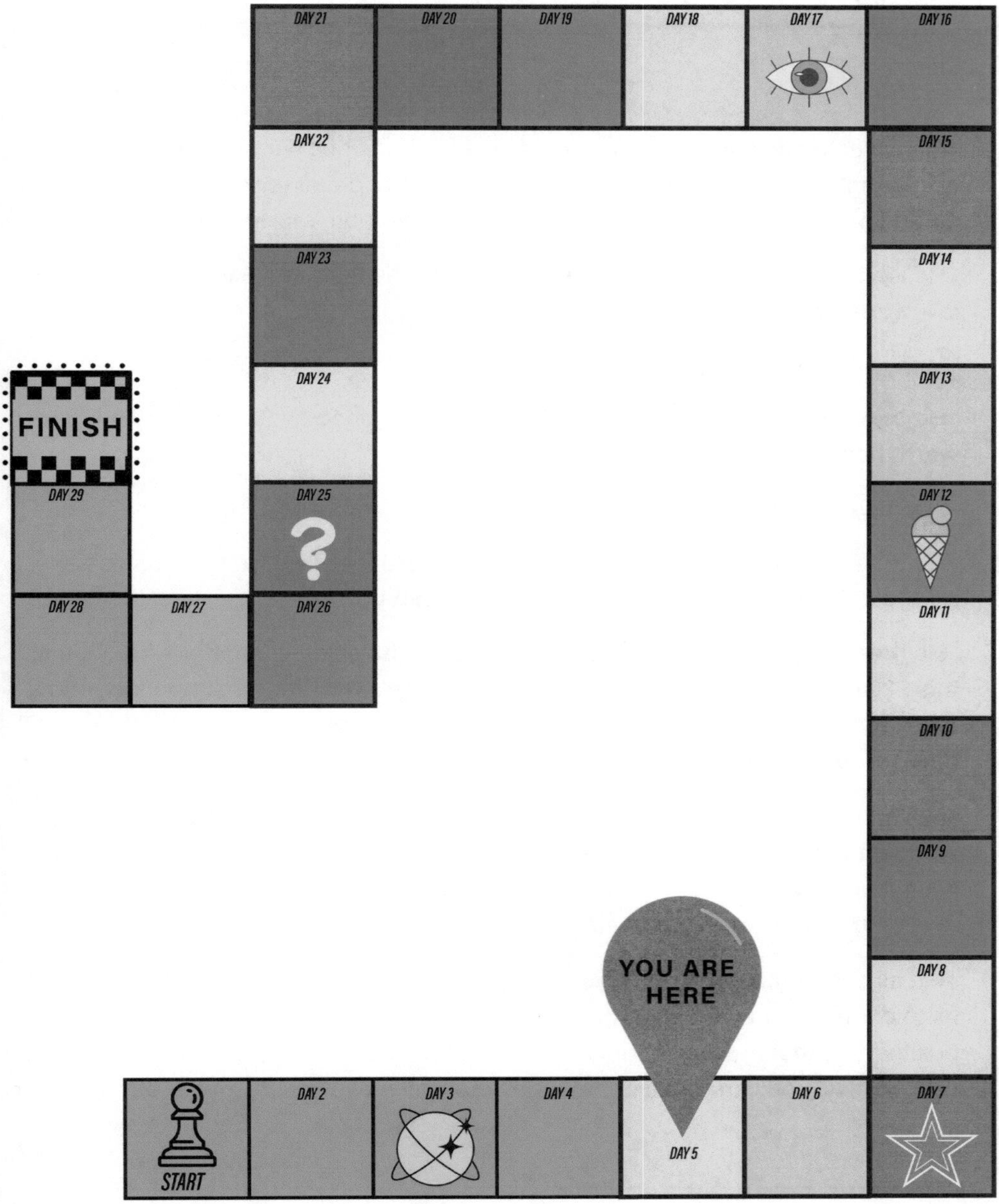
START
DAY 2
DAY 3
DAY 4
DAY 5
YOU ARE HERE
DAY 6
DAY 7
DAY 8
DAY 9
DAY 10
DAY 11
DAY 12
DAY 13
DAY 14
DAY 15
DAY 16
DAY 17
DAY 18
DAY 19
DAY 20
DAY 21
DAY 22
DAY 23
DAY 24
DAY 25
DAY 26
DAY 27
DAY 28
DAY 29
FINISH

KNOW YOUR WORTH

Many years ago I saw a speaker captivate his audience with a simple but powerful example on value. He held a $20 bill in his hand and raised his arm up in the air and asked,"Who wants this $20?" Many in the room raised their hands.

He lowered his arm and then threw the bill on the floor and asked, "How much is it worth now?"

Many yelled, "$20!"

He then stepped on it and proceeded to twist his shoe on it. "How much is it worth now?" he asked again.

And again, "$20!" yelled the crowd.

He then grabbed it off the floor, crumpled it, held it out on the palm of his hand and yelled, "Now, who still wants it?" Hands shot up.

He then paused, nodded his head in approval and said,"No matter what I did to this $20 it still held its value. This should serve as a reminder that no matter how many times your dreams are crumpled, how many friends toss you aside, you still have value."

I love this example because it's a reminder we all have something to offer the world and to those around us regardless of how they may treat us. Never attach your value to what others say about you or do to you. Be more concerned with what you do and say to yourself.

We all carry emotional scars from the past; things done to us that still cause us to cringe. And every time we give the past credence, we undermine our own positive psychology and by default our happiness and success today. What's the ONE THING you can begin doing today that will move you past your past?

_____

_____

_____

DAY 6

One thing to get done...

DAY 7

You landed on a Reward Day!

Do absolutely nothing! Sometimes the best reward is simply permission to relax without any guilt. Take a nap, stay in your pajamas all day, or just veg out on the couch.

DAY 7

One thing to get done...

DAY 8

One thing to get done...

DAY 9

One thing to get done...

DON'T STOP JUMPING

One day there was a group of frogs leaping through the forest enjoying themselves. All of sudden, two of the many frogs leapt over a log without realizing the giant hole behind it. Down they went crashing down into the deep hole. The other frogs gather around the hole to see if what happened and to check on their two comrades. They realized that the hole was far to deep for them to ever leap out of to save themselves. Yet, the two frogs were leaping feverishly trying to get out of the hole. The both took turns trying to leap out of the hole but with little success.

The group of frogs atop arrived at the conclusion that their two friends were doomed. "Stop jumping! You'll never get out! Accept your fate!", they all yelled down the hole.

Upon hearing this, one of the frogs in the hole decided to stop jumping and accepted his fate. The other frog, a bit more stubborn, kept jumping.

They continued to yell down the hole, "Stop jumping! You'll never get out! Accept your fate!" But the stubborn frog kept jumping and then, summoning all his might, he jumped one more time and leapt out of the hole to the disbelief of all the frogs atop.

With an incredulous tone one of the frogs who was yelling down the hole asked, "Hey, didn't you hear us yelling at you while you were down there?"

The stubborn frog said, "What was that?"

"I said, didn't you hear us yelling at you telling you it was impossible to get out?" he repeated.

"Oh!" said the stubborn frog, "I'm a bit deaf. I thought you guys were cheering me on." In the end one frog chose to listen to the naysayers and his fate was sealed in that hole. The stubborn frog refused to give up because he couldn't hear the negativity of others.

Too often in life, in order for you to be successful, you have to turn a deaf ear to the naysayers and never stop jumping. The hole is only as deep as you believe it is.

Is there something(s) you stopped or quit doing because you listened to others?

What are they? List them and ask yourself which ones are worth jumping for.

_____

_____

_____

_____

_____

DAY 10

One thing to get done...

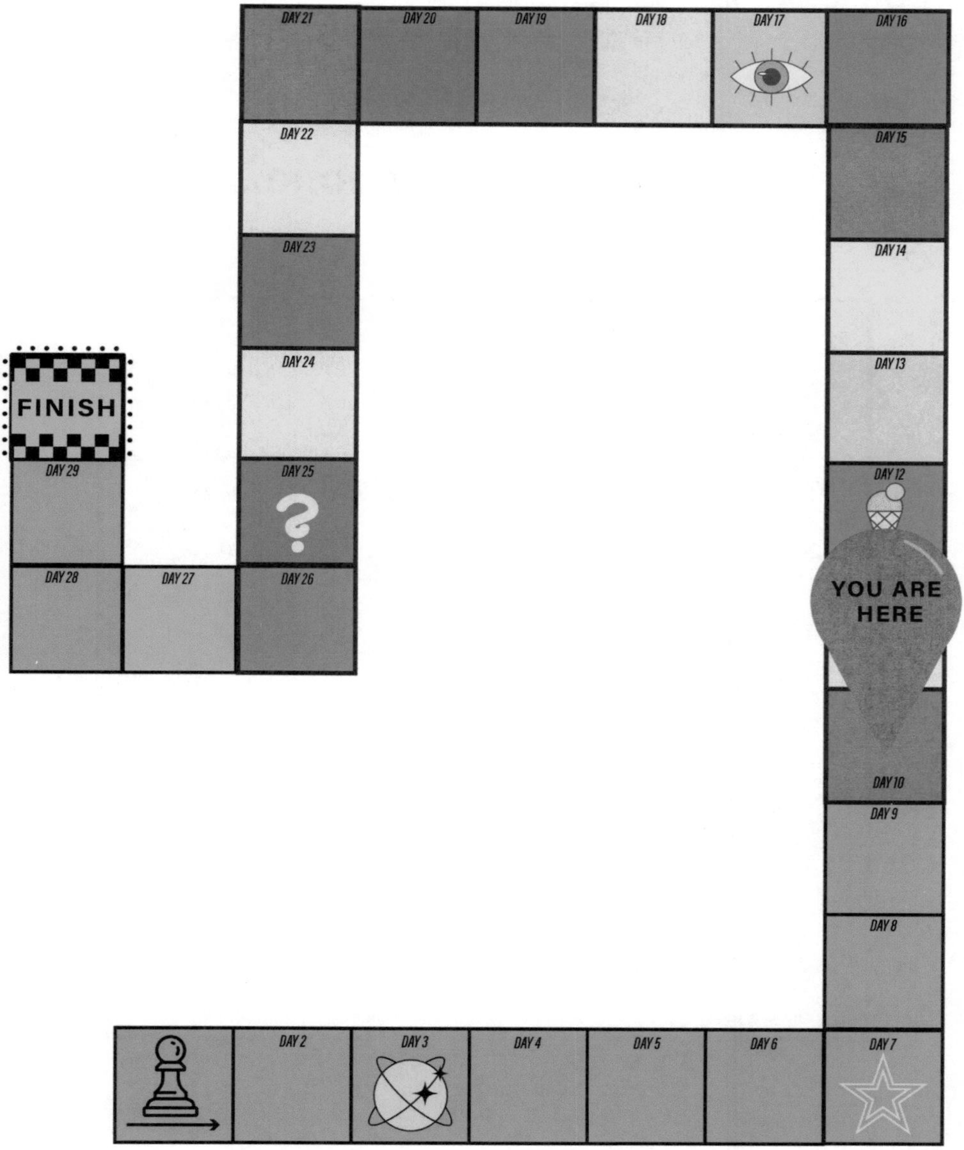

DAY 2
DAY 3
DAY 4
DAY 5
DAY 6
DAY 7
DAY 8
DAY 9
DAY 10
YOU ARE HERE
DAY 12
DAY 13
DAY 14
DAY 15
DAY 16
DAY 17
DAY 18
DAY 19
DAY 20
DAY 21
DAY 22
DAY 23
DAY 24
DAY 25
DAY 26
DAY 27
DAY 28
DAY 29
FINISH

DAY 11

One thing to get done...

DAY 12

You landed on a Reward Day!

Grab a coffee or tea from your favorite shop, enjoy a delicious pastry, or savor a scoop of ice cream.

DAY12

One thing to get done...

DAY 13

One thing to get done...

MISFITS

So I decided to watch Rudolph the Red Nose Reindeer with my little girl who had never seen the original claymation movie I grew up with. It premiered on December 6th, 1964, and has become the longest running, highest rated television special in the history of the medium. If you recall, Herbie on of the elves, is distracted while on the toy assembly line. Herbie's job is to paint the wooden trucks coming his way. The supervising elf yells at him and asks him why he's falling behind and Herbie confesses to the supervising elf that he doesn't like making toys.

In disbelief the headelf yells, "What!? You don't like making toys?"

Herbie replies, "I want to be a dentist." The whole floor laughs at Herbie and the supervisor shoves a load of wooden trucks in front of Herbie and says, "You're an elf. And elves make toys."

Herbie, unhappy, later on decides to runaway as he realizes he doesn't belong there; he considers himself a misfit He meets up with Rudolph, who also considers himself a misfit and together they run away.

While trekking through the snowstorm, they discover the Land of Misfit Toys; a place where toys go when no child wants them. Herbie and Ruldoph promise the King of Misfit Land that they'll return with Santa who will find homes for these misfit toys; and they do.

In the movie, both Herbie and Rudolph set out NOT knowing: who, what, where and when. The only thing they knew was the ' Why"; to pursue their dreams. Motivated by unhappiness when they set out, they had no idea how they were going to achieve their goals; they just did it.

If you're unhappy with your job maybe it's because you're not a fit. And guess what? It's OK not to fit in, and be different.

It's OK to be a misfit.

The objective in life is to find your 'fit' where you belong. Be proud of being a misfit! And keep in mind that a misfit is only a misfit until he or she finds their fit!

Are you doing what makes you happy? If not, what would you rather be doing?

_____

_____

_____

_____

DAY 14

One thing to get done...

DAY 15

One thing to get done...

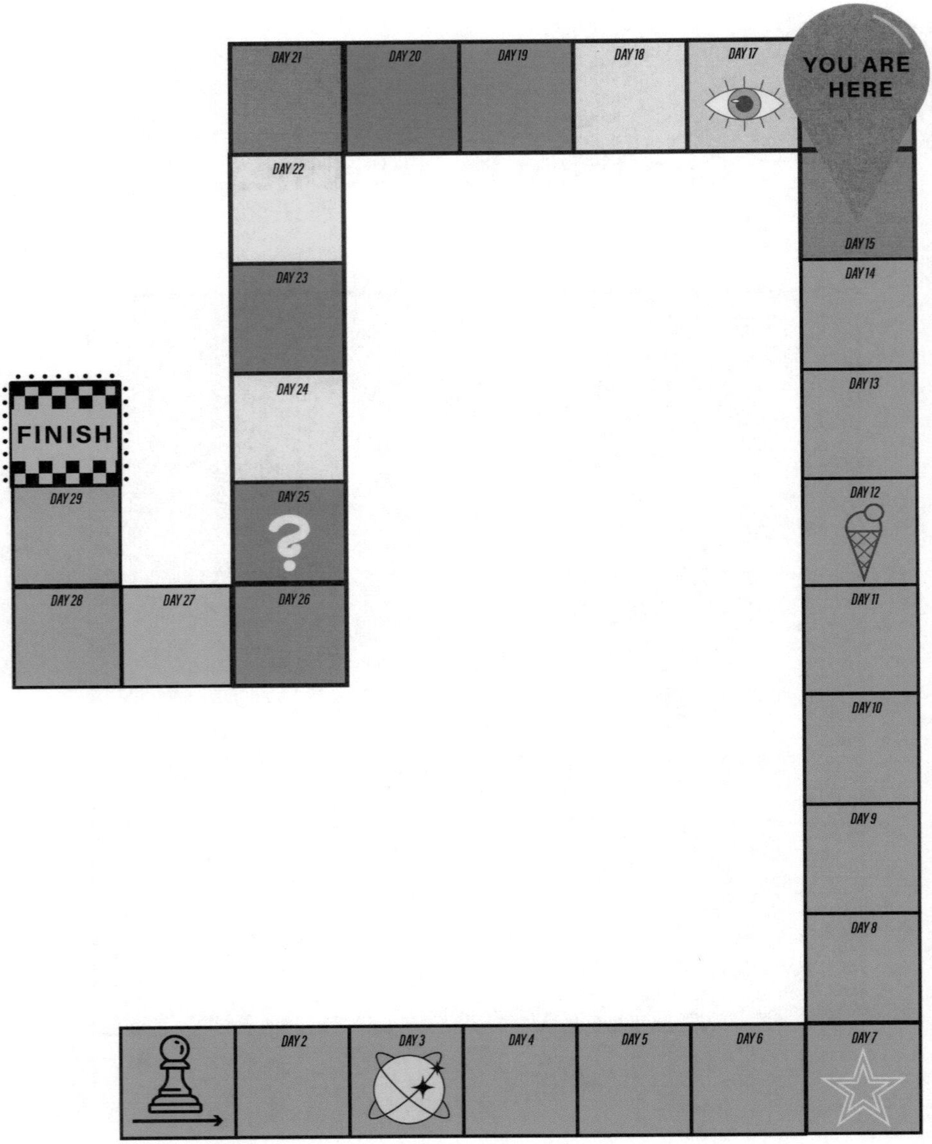

DAY 2
DAY 3
DAY 4
DAY 5
DAY 6
DAY 7
DAY 8
DAY 9
DAY 10
DAY 11
DAY 12
DAY 13
DAY 14
DAY 15
YOU ARE HERE
DAY 17
DAY 18
DAY 19
DAY 20
DAY 21
DAY 22
DAY 23
DAY 24
DAY 25
DAY 26
DAY 27
DAY 28
DAY 29
FINISH

DAY 16

One thing to get done...

DAY 17

You landed on a Reward Day!

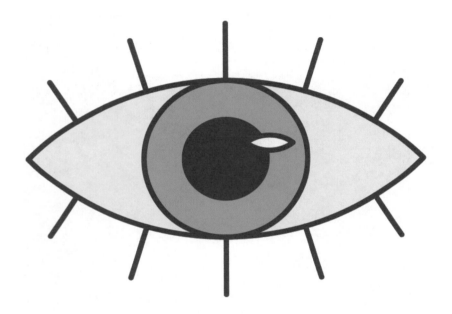

Create a vision board or scrap book of goals you want to acheive, places you want to go, and all-around inspirational motivation for the future.

DAY 17

One thing to get done...

DAY18

One thing to get done...

DAY 19

One thing to get done...

STOP PECKING AT CRUMBS

Year ago I was made Vice President of Sales for Latin America and it was the company's desire that I live in the region. We had offices throughout the region and I chose, Buenos Aires, Argentina. I had never lived outside the U.S. so I knew it would be a cultural adventure for my family and myself; and it was!

I quickly learned that Argentines like to talk business but they also want to get to know you; relationships count! Downtown Buenos Aires is littered with small cafes where it was common to grab un cafecito y una media luna (a cup of coffee and a crescent roll) and chat as the traffic and people went by. One day at a café I was chatting with my new friend Jorge. I noticed every time some crumbs fell from the table pigeons would swoop down to clean up and then fly away. After witnessing this swoop in and out routine a few times I decided to grab a big chunk of bread and put it on the ground and give the pigeons a real meal. To my surprise not one pigeon swooped down. Jorge and I shrugged it off. And as soon as some crumbs fell off the nearby table the pigeons swooped down for clean up.

On my way home that evening I reflected on why the pigeons didn't go for the big chunk of bread but always flew down for the crumbs. Then it hit me; they're use to eating crumbs! The pigeons are not accustomed to seeing big pieces of bread, they're use to (conditioned to) eating crumbs. That thought led me to think more about success and opportunity.

Could it be that the reason many people find success elusive is that they're so accustomed to seeing (eating) crumbs that when an opportunity (the big bread) presents itself they've developed a blind spot, much like the pigeons, and they miss it?

I heard someone once say, "If you think small, you'll always stay small. If you think big, you can be big."

The key to peering around your blind spot it to raise your expectations of what you want. Simply put, think big to see big!

DAY 20

One thing to get done...

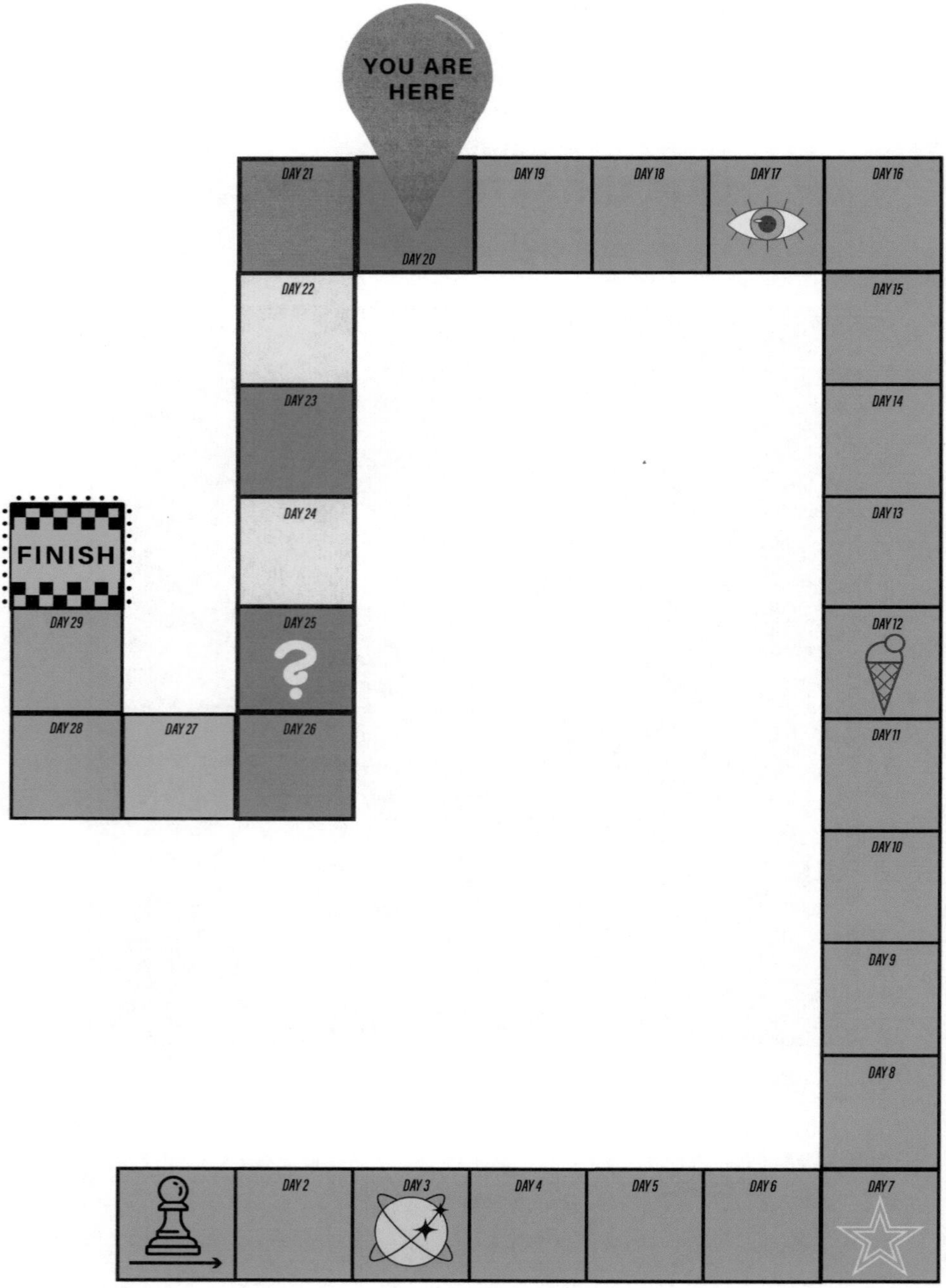
YOU ARE HERE
DAY 2
DAY 3
DAY 4
DAY 5
DAY 6
DAY 7
DAY 8
DAY 9
DAY 10
DAY 11
DAY 12
DAY 13
DAY 14
DAY 15
DAY 16
DAY 17
DAY 18
DAY 19
DAY 20
DAY 21
DAY 22
DAY 23
DAY 24
DAY 25
DAY 26
DAY 27
DAY 28
DAY 29
FINISH

DAY 21

One thing to get done...

THIS IS GOOD!

Once upon a time there was a king who loved to go hunting in the royal forest. He had a servant who was very faithful and yet had the annoying habit of stating, "This is good!" when something happened; good or bad. The king tolerated him because he was so loyal.

One day the king and his servant were hunting in the woods. The king spotted the prey so the loyal servant hands him the shotgun. When the king fired the gun, it jammed in such a way that it backfired and blew one of the king's fingers completely off.

As the king writhed in pain the servant began yelling, "This is good! This is good!" The king, irritated and angry, ordered that his faithful servant be thrown in jail.

A year later while hunting in the forest by himself, the king came across a group of cannibals who quickly captured him and began preparing him for their meal. As they did so, one of the cannibals noticed he was missing a finger. Cannibals consider people who are not 'whole' bad luck to eat so they let the king go.

Overjoyed, the king returned to his castle and went to directly to the dungeon to release his loyal servant whom he'd blamed for his missing finger and had jailed a year back. Upon the servant's release the king relayed the story of the cannibals and why they had let him go. He then apologized profusely to the servant for throwing in jail.

The servant replied, "No need to apologize for jailing me; this is good!"

Confused the king asked, "How can me throwing you in jail be good?"

The servant reminded the king that if he had been with the king at the time he was capture by the cannibals they would've let the king go and eaten him, "So this is good!"

The takeaway from this story is that when things don't go your way, maybe, just maybe you should adopt the servant's mantra, "This is good."

For example, you get fired from your job.

This is good! Why? You later land a better one.

Your spouse leaves. This is good! Why? You find a better mate who appreciates you. This is good!

Think of a time(s) where you were hurt by someone, or something, but in the end it turned out to be a blessing in disguise.

_____

_____

_____

_____

DAY 22

One thing to get done...

DAY 23

One thing to get done...

PEOPLE PLEASING

Once upon a time in a small village lived a man with his son who owned a farm and would travel into town every week to sell their produce. On one particular trip into town, the father told his son to ride on top of the horse that was pulling the small wagon loaded with produce. The son obliged. As they entered the town, there was an old man standing near the entrance to the market. As the father and the son passed by, the old man commented aloud, "How could it be, how could it be, the son rides the horse and the father suffers the walk. Poor, poor father." They both did their best to ignore the old man.

The following week, the son insisted that his father ride the horse into town and he would walk instead. The father agreed. As they entered the town, the old man was there again and upon seeing the father riding the horse said aloud, "How could it be, how could it be, the father rides the horse and the son suffers the walk. Poor, poor son." They both again did their best to ignore the old man.

Before heading into town the following week, the father and son decided that they would both ride atop of the horse into town. As they approached the entrance, the same old man said, "How could it be, how could it be, both the father and son ride atop the horse. Poor, poor horse."

The moral of the story is clear; that no matter what the father and son did, the old man would never be satisfied. We spend so much time and energy trying to please others to no avail. We bend over backwards to do them favors, we sacrifice our own time (and money), and they're still not happy. You can't please all the people all the time, but trying to do so only results in both parties being miserable. They're miserable because that's their natural state and you're miserable because it seems like no matter what you do or try, they simply don't appreciate your efforts.

In the end, living to please others is a losing strategy.

Think of a time when you went out of your way to help someone and they still complained or didn't acknowledge your efforts.

_____

_____

_____

_____

DAY 24

One thing to get done...

DAY 25

You landed on a Reward Day!

Watch a documentary on a topic that interests you, listen to a podcast, or take a short online course.

DAY 25

One thing to get done...

DAY 26

One thing to get done...

DAY 27

One thing to get done...

WHINING: BEMOANING SUCCESS

There once was an old man who lived in a small shack off the side of a long, dusty road. The man loved to sit on the front porch in his favorite rocking chair with his faithful hound dog that always lay next to the chair. One day while rocking in his chair, a stranger came along and approached the old man's house, asking if he wouldn't mind sparing a glass of water. The old-timer agreed and went inside while the hound dog just lay there motionless.

As he waited for the old-timer to return, the hound dog let out a long moan. When the old man returned with the water, he struck up a conversation with his visitor. The stranger began to notice that during the course of the conversation with the old man, the old dog would occasionally let out a long moan. The stranger did everything to ignore the old hound and concentrate on the friendly conversation.

Finally, the stranger could no longer resist the urge to ask, "Excuse me, old-timer, but why is your hound dog moaning? Is he sick?"

"Nah, he ain't sick. He's groaning like that because he's lying down on a nail," replied the old-timer.

"A nail?"

"Yep, a nail."

The stranger looked perplexed, "Well, why doesn't he just get up off it?"

The old-timer shot back, "You see, stranger, even though the nail hurts him, it doesn't hurt him enough to make him want to get up."

Much like the hound dog, too many people spend their days complaining (moaning) about how bad their job is, how they don't have enough money to buy things, or how their dreams seem to be slipping away. You have a choice! You can continue to lie atop your nail of discontent (i.e., whining about what if...) or you can decide to stop the whining, take action, and begin to change your circumstance.

What have you been talking about for years that you haven't taken action on? Why haven't you started?

_____

_____

_____

_____

DAY 28

One thing to get done...

DAY 29

One thing to get done...

DAY 30

DONE!

You did it! You've completed 30 days of "One Thing Done"!

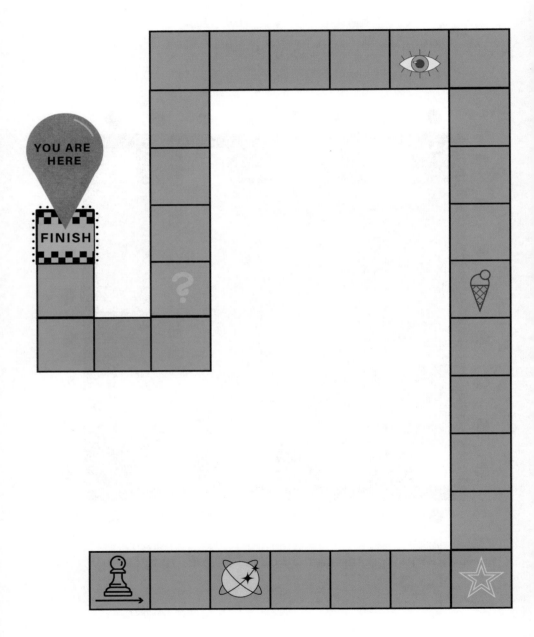

What goal did you accomplish by the end of 30 days?

_____

_____

_____

_____

_____

Write 3 things you learned about yourself.

_____

_____

_____

_____

_____

What is your next goal?

_____

_____

_____

_____

_____

Notes:

Made in the USA
Columbia, SC
02 May 2024